LEARNING TOGETHER

ADVICE AND INSTRUCTIONS ON COMPLETING THESE TESTS

1. There are 100 questions in each test. Make sure you have not missed a page.

2. Start at question 1 and work your way to question 100.

3. If you are unable to complete a question leave it and go to the next one.

4. Do not think about the question you have just left as this wastes time.

5. If you change an answer make sure the change is clear.

6. Make sure you spell correctly.

7. You may do any rough work on the test paper or on another piece of paper.

8. Each test should take approximately 50 minutes.

9. When you have finished each test mark it with an adult.

10. An adult or parent may be able to explain any questions you do not understand.

TEST 11 *

SCORE _____

1. Write down any letter which occurs 3 times in REVERBERANT and once in RESONANT. (_____)

2. Write down any letter which occurs once in RADIOGRAPHER and once in RADIOLOGIST. (_____)

3. Which letter occurs in JOANNE but not in JOAN ? (_____)

4. A number plus one third of six equals 10. What is the number ? (_____)

Share 15 apples between Janet and John so that for every ONE apple Janet gets John gets TWO apples.

5. How many apples does John get ? (_____)

6. How many apples does Janet get ? (_____)

7. How many less than John did Janet get ? (_____)

In each sentence below TWO words must change places to make the sentence sensible. In each sentence underline the TWO words which must change places. An example has been done to help you.

The <u>wood</u> was made of <u>table</u>.

8. The fan had broken its car belt.

9. When they climbed to the rain the top had stopped.

10. The ship sailed anchor and lifted away.

11. A page was note from the torn book.

12. What dinner we having for our are to-day ?

The table below gives some information about the addition of numbers in the left hand column to numbers in the top row. Complete the table.

+	0.3	2.2	1.4
0.7	1.0	2.9	2.1
1.6	1.9		
1.2	1.5		

13, 14. (row 1.6)

15, 16. (row 1.2)

TEST 11 PAGE 1.

In the following write in the brackets one letter which will complete the word in front of the brackets AND the word after the brackets.

Here is an example.   ROA (D) OOR.

17. BOTTO (__) OUSE.   18. CA   (__) AT.

19. VER   (__) ACHT.   20. CRIS (__) RICE.

21. WRIN (__) RAIN.   22. BEN (__) EAR.

Complete the sequences by inserting the correct numbers or letters in the brackets.

A B C D E F G H I J K L M N O P Q R S T U V W X Y Z

23.	A	D	F	I	(_____)
24.	ZY	WV	SR	NM	(_____)
25.	FGH	EFG	DEF	CDE	(_____)
26.	WV	TU	SR	PQ	(_____)
27.	1.5	3.0	4.5	6.0	(_____)
28.	25	21	17	13	(_____)
29.	162	54	18	6	(_____)
30.	9.8	10.9	12	13.1	(_____)

In each line below a word from the left-hand group joins with one from the right-hand group to make a new word. The left-hand word always comes first.
Underline the chosen words. An example has been done to help you.

CORN FARM TIME   OVER FIELD YARD

31.	FOR	LONG	DAM	TELL	CAST	SAKE
32.	BLISS	DEEP	DAM	TEAR	PEN	SELL
33.	ROBE	JERK	TALK	ART	IN	LIKE
34.	PASS	FEW	PAD	ABLE	ILL	DOCK
35.	TAB	OVER	INN	LET	TUNE	LOW
36.	TALE	ON	MAN	TILL	OR	TELL

In the sentences below there are 4 words missing. Choose the **MOST SUITABLE** words from the lists A to D to complete the sentences. Choose a word from list A for space A, a word from list B for space B and so on. <u>Underline the words you choose</u>.

As the weather got more (A) we (B) together to try to keep (C).
Paul was shivering with fear and we hoped that soon the people would leave their homes and begin to (D) for us.

(37) A	(38) B	(39) C	(40) D
pleasant	cried	dry	pray
wet	walked	warm	hope
miserable	shivered	hungry	talk
deteriorate	laughed	awake	search
hot	huddled	asleep	cry

£43.97 was made up using the smallest number of notes and coins shown below. How many of each were used ?

41. £10 notes (_____)   42. 50p coins (_____)   43. 20p coins (_____)

44. 2p coins (_____)   45. 1p coins (_____)

Thermometers are drawn below. The arrows point to temperatures. Read the temperatures and enter them into the brackets below the thermometers.

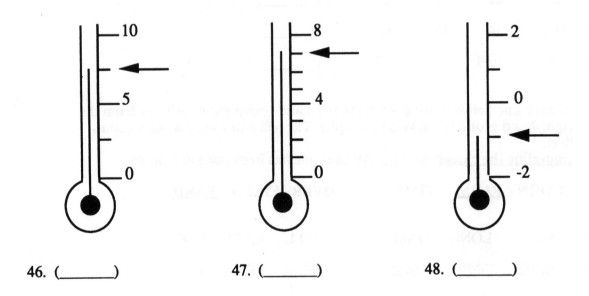

46. (_____)   47. (_____)   48. (_____)

Arrange the following words in alphabetical order.

enclose,   emery,   emend,   enamel,   emerge.

(_____) (_____) (_____) (_____) (_____)
First   last
  49.   50.   51.   52.   53.

Oldborough School has three lessons each afternoon. Each lesson except the second lesson lasts for the same length of time. There is a 5 minute gap between each lesson. Complete the table below, which shows the times at which lessons begin and end ?

		Begins	Ends
54.	First Lesson	1.25 pm	
55.	Second Lesson		2.35 pm
56.	Third Lesson		3.15 pm

In the following questions a letter can be taken from the first word and put into the second word to form TWO new words. Write both NEW words.

Example. THEN   TANK   (TEN) (THANK)

The H moves from THEN to TANK and makes the new words TEN and THANK.

57.   LATHER   TICK   (_____) (_____)

58.   FIORD   BAT   (_____) (_____)

59.   RINSE   KIT   (_____) (_____)

60.   LANCE   HARM   (_____) (_____)

61.   THERM   GALLEY   (_____) (_____)

62.   MAIZE   NOSE   (_____) (_____)

A man sells consecutively numbered tickets from a roll of tickets. The first number he sells is 0234 and the last ticket he sells is 0436

63. How many tickets did he sell ?   (_____)

64. If he had sold 300 tickets what would have been the number of the next ticket not sold ?   (_____)

In each question below a man ALWAYS STARTS by facing NORTH.
What direction would he be facing if -

65. He turned a quarter turn clockwise followed by a three-quarter turn anti-clockwise?   (_____)

66. He made a three-quarter turn clockwise, followed by a half turn anti-clockwise, and then a quarter turn clockwise ?   (_____)

67. He turned through 360 degrees ?   (_____)

Six boys A, B, C, D, E and F sit equally spaced around a circular table.
D sits on A's right and opposite E. C sits between A and E. B sits on the
left of the person opposite A. B then changes places with A and C
changes places with D.

68. Who now sits on the left of B ?   (_____)

69. Who now sits opposite the person on the left of D ?   (_____)

70. Who is furthest away from B ?   (_____)

F leaves the room and the rest of the boys change seats.
A and E swop places, B moves to the seat opposite.
E moves 2 seats to the left and C moves to an empty chair.

71. Who is sitting to the left of an empty chair ?   (_____)

72. Who is sitting between B and D ?   (_____)

73. F returns and sits at the table. Who is on his left ?   (_____)

Five children A, B, C, D and E return from holiday with sticks of rock,
postcards and toys as presents. Only B and D didn't have sticks of rock.
B was the only person with just one present and it was a postcard.
Only A and E did not have postcards. 4 children had toys.

74. Who brought only a postcard and toys home ?   (_____)

75. Who brought 3 presents home ?   (_____)

76. Which 2 children had the same presents?   (_____)

77. Altogether how many presents were taken home ?   (_____)

In each of the following questions one word can be put in front of each
of the given words to form a new word or phrase.
Write the correct word in the brackets. An example is shown to help you.

shell   shore   side   bird   (SEA)

78. get   land   night   summer   (_____)

79. dog   fire   powder   boat   (_____)

80. cast   pour   stream   trodden   (_____)

81. look   coat   throw   haul   (_____)

In each of the following questions the numbers in the second column are
formed from the numbers in the first column by using the same rule. Put the
correct answer in the bracket for each question.

82. 6 ----> 12

    7 ----> 14

    8 ----> 16

    9 ----> (___)

83. 36 ----> 5

    25 ----> 4

    81 ----> 8

    49 ----> (___)

84. 5 ----> 12

    6 ----> 14

    10 ----> 22

    17 ----> (___)

85. 18 ----> 8

    14 ----> 6

    12 ----> 5

    6 ----> (___)

86. 1 ----> 1

    3 ----> 27

    4 ----> 64

    5 ----> (___)

87. 2 ----> 3

    4 ----> 9

    7 ----> 18

    10 ----> (___)

In the diagrams below each of the small rectangles are the same size.
What fraction of each diagram is shaded ?

88. (_____)

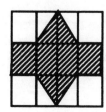

89. (_____)

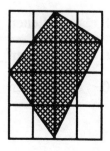

In each line below, the first word can be changed into the last word in three stages. Only one letter can be replaced at a time and proper words must be made each time.   An example has been done to help you.

tide   (ride) (rode) rope

90.   hail   (_____) (_____)   pull

91.   pink   (_____) (_____)   cane

92.   fact   (_____) (_____)   lake

93.   kerb   (_____) (_____)   head

94.   chin   (_____) (_____)   shop

The numbers on a die (a single dice) are covered by 6 different letters of the alphabet

Four of the letters are vowels.
The letter I is the only vowel which covers an even number.
The number 2 is covered by the letter which comes immediately after the third vowel used.
The sum of the numbers, which are covered by consonants, is 6.
The first and last letters of the alphabet are used and the sum of the numbers they cover is 7.
The largest odd number is covered by the vowel which is nearest to the middle of the alphabet and the other vowels appear near the beginning of the alphabet.

Beside each number below write the letter which covers it on the die.

95.   1.   Letter _____

96.   2.   Letter _____

97.   3.   Letter _____

98.   4.   Letter _____

99.   5.   Letter _____

100.   6.   Letter _____

TEST 12 *

SCORE _____

1. Which letter, occurring more than once, occurs as often in GEOSYNCLINE as it does in GENTLEMEN ? (_____)

2. Which letter occurs once in HUNDREDWEIGHT, once in KILOGRAM and twice in WEIGHING ? (_____)

3. Which letter occurs as often in LAWLESS as it does in LAW-MAKER but does not occur in JUDGE ? (_____)

4. Charles adds 9 to a third of a number and gets 27. What is half of that number ? (_____)

5. Books cost 7p. more than comics. Two books and one comic cost 53p. How much for one comic ? (_____)

In the questions below TWO words must change places so that the sentence makes sense. Underline the TWO words that must change places.

Look at this example: The <u>wood</u> was made of <u>table</u>.

6. The television turned the child on.

7. The man hung the picture framed on the wall.

8. The sun soon dried and blistered in the paint.

9. A computer program pressed the wrong button and lost the operator.

10. His present told him to choose a mother and put it in the car.

**The table below gives some information about the addition of numbers in the left hand column to those in the top row.
Complete the table correctly using only the numbers given.**

28.75,   22.7,   5.1,   35.95,   2.5,   27.3.

+		9.7	
17.6			20.1
26.25	31.35		

11, 12. (first row)
13, 14. (second row)
15, 16. (third row)

**In each line below write in the brackets one letter which completes the word in front of and the word after the brackets.
Look at this example: ROA (D) OOR**

Here D completes ROAD and begins DOOR.

17. FOREIG   (____)   EWT

18. CRA   (____)   NU

19. ELUD   (____)   LBOW

20. GEA   (____)   EIGN

21. SOCIA   (____)   IBEL

5 kings Alfred, Charles, William, Harold and George all had different amounts of money.

William is not the richest or the poorest but is richer than at least 2 other kings. Alfred is only richer than one other king and that is not Harold or George. George is poorer than 1 other king and that is not Charles.

List the kings from richest to poorest.

22.　(＿＿＿＿＿＿＿＿) richest

23.　(＿＿＿＿＿＿)

24.　(＿＿＿＿＿＿)

25.　(＿＿＿＿＿＿)

26.　(＿＿＿＿＿＿) poorest

In each line below underline TWO words, ONE from each side, which together make ONE correctly spelt word. The word on the left always comes first.

Look at this example:

BLACK ALL TOP　　　AND **BIRD** BOY

27.	DO	NO	AS		NOW	SENT	ICE
28.	BAG	BOOK	KNOW		AGE	LED	CASE
29.	PAGE	GLOW	FAR		ANT	BEE	ASS
30.	PLOUGH	STIR	HERE		RING	UP	ON
31.	BUD	ADD	SUIT		ON	IN	OR
32.	VICAR	WEST	STUN		AGE	LAW	ANT

A number of people sit evenly spaced around a circular table. They are numbered consecutively in an anti-clockwise direction. Number 9 sits opposite the person who is two places to the left of number 6.

33.　How many people are at the table ?　　　　　(＿＿＿)

34.　Which number is opposite number 1 ?　　　　(＿＿＿)

35.　Which number is beside number 2 and opposite number 8 ?　(＿＿＿)

36,37. Number 3 and number 9 change places. Which two numbers now sit beside number 10 ?　　　　　　(＿＿,＿＿)

Write in the brackets a word that rhymes with the second word and has a similar meaning to the first word.

Look at this example:

SICK   MILL   (___ILL___)

38. ANSWER   STY   (_____)

39. LIFT   HAZE   (_____)

40. CROWD   ROB   (_____)

In the paragraph below five words are missing. Choose the most appropriate words from the lists below. One word from list A fills the space at A, one word from list B fills the space at B and so on.

Underline the word you choose.

The Hallowe'en fireworks (A) into the cold (B) night. The children (C) with amazement as the rockets burst into a (D) of brilliant colours and lit up the (E) night sky.

41A	42B	43C	44D	45E
SLID	CHRISTMAS	GASPED	RIVER	BRIGHT
JUMPED	OCTOBER	SHOUTED	MIDDLE	WET
EXPLODED	FEBRUARY	HID	CASCADE	CLOUDY
FELL	EASTER	WHISPERED	STREAM	DAWN
HURRIED	JULY	SANG	PUDDLE	DARK

In each question below one letter can be removed from the word in the first column and put into the word in the second column to give two new words. The order of the letters is not changed.

Look at this example:

THINS   TOUT   (THIN)   (STOUT)

46. TREAT   PINT   (_____)   (_____)

47. FIND   RUM   (_____)   (_____)

48. VOICE   WING   (_____)   (_____)

49. GNASH   LINE   (_____)   (_____)

50. BLACK   RUE   (_____)   (_____)

Complete the sequence by inserting the correct number in the brackets.

51. 23.37, 23.45, 23.53, 00.01   (_____)

52. 4.15, 3.25, 2.35, 1.45   (_____)

53. (34,43), (41,35), (48,27), (55,19)   (____,____)

54. 2, 7, 14, 23, 34   (_____)

55. 1024, 256, 64, 16   (_____)

Using the numbers 8, 5, 6 and 4 ONCE ONLY in each question, fill in the spaces in any way that will make the statements correct.
An example is shown to help you.

$$(\_8\_ + \_5\_ + \_6\_ + \_4\_) = 23$$

56. (____ X ____) - (____ X ____)   = 28

57. (____ + ____ + ____) X (____)   = 76

58. (____ - ____) - (____ - ____)   = 1

59. (____ + ____) X (____ + ____)   = 130

60. (____ X ____) - (____ + ____)   = 11

In questions 61-66 the three words A, B and C are in alphabetical order.
The word at B is missing and you are given a dictionary definition instead.
Write the correct word in the space.
Look at this example: A) FLAP
                     B) (__FLARE__) Distress signal from a boat.
                     C) FLASH

61. A) ANVIL
     B) (_____) Uneasy with fear.
     C) ANY

62. A) PLACK
     B) (_____) A deadly epidemic.
     C) PLAICE

63. A) FOUND
     B) (_____) A jet of water.
     C) FOUR

64. A) HIPPODROME
     B) (____) To engage for wages.
     C) HIRSEL

65. A) JABBER
     B) (_____) A wild, dog-like animal.
     C) JACKAROO

66. A) MOUSSE
     B) (_____) Opening in the head of an animal.
     C) MOVE

In each question 67-70 the numbers in the second column are formed from the numbers in the first column by using a certain rule. Put the correct answer opposite the arrow. A different rule is used in each question.

67. 5------>26
      6------>37
      7------>50
      8------>

68. 12------>15
      16------>20
      20------>25
      28------>

69. 1------>0
      2------>7
      3------>14
      6------>

70. 5------>17
      80------>242
      7------>23
      90------>

From the following shapes select the shape or shapes which satisfy the statements given. They may satisfy the statement on all or on some occasions. Answer the questions by placing the letter of the shape or shapes in the brackets.

A
PARRALLELOGRAM

B
RECTANGLE

C
SQUARE

D
TRIANGLE

E
TRAPEZIUM

71. Diagonals are of equal length.   (_____)

72. Diagonals are at right angles.   (_____)

73. Three different sized sides.   (_____)

74. Internal angles total 180 degrees.   (_____)

The numbers 1, 2, 3, 4, 5, 6 and 7 are used in code form to produce the words:

BRASH   ERASER   RASHER   SHARP   PHRASE

One of the words uses 1, 2, 3, 4 and 5 for its first five letters.
Two of the words have a 3 for their last but one letter.
A five letter word begins with 6.

75. What is PHRASE in code ?   (_____)

76. What is ERASER in code ?   (_____)

77. What is BRASH in code ?   (_____)

78. What word does 152751 represent ?   (_____)

79. If an 8 means L then what word does 75218 represent ?   (_____)

80. What word does 82658 represent ?   (_____)

4 boys Peter, Andrew, Mark and Billy build model cars from parts which are red, blue, green and yellow. The cars have tyres, radios, boots and bonnets. Each car contains 4 parts and each part is a different colour. There is only one part of each colour and no car contains any two parts which are the same colour.

Andrew's tyres are the same colour as Peter's radio and Mark's bonnet.
Andrew's boot is yellow.
Mark's radio is the same colour as Peter's boot and Andrew's bonnet.
Peter's tyres and Billy's bonnet are red.
Mark's radio is green.

81. Who has a car with a blue radio ?   (_____)

82. Who has a car with green tyres ?   (_____)

83. Who has a car with a yellow bonnet ?   (_____)

84. What colour are Mark's tyres ?   (_____)

85. What colour is Peter's bonnet ?   (_____)

86. What colour is Billy's radio ?   (_____)

A man is tiling a table top using rectangular and square plastic tiles. He uses a pattern like that shown in the diagram. The rectangular tile "A" measures 15 x 5 cms.

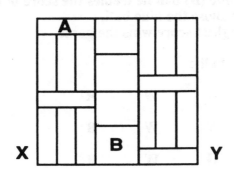

87. What is the distance X---->Y ?   (_____cms)

88. What is the area of a square tile B ?   (_____sq.cms.)

89. How many tiles would be needed if the sides of the pattern were trebled in length ?   (_____tiles)

90. The man finds that he can only buy square tiles which measure 5 x 5 cms. He cannot buy rectangular tiles. How many small square tiles would he need to fill the diagram above ?   (_____tiles)

91. Small square tiles cost 60p for a packet of 12 or 8p for a single tile. How much would it cost the man to buy the tiles that he uses in question number 90 if he buys as many full packets of twelve tiles as possible ?   (_____)

A man on holiday in Spain cashes a cheque for £100 and receives 18800 pesetas. (In each question below the exchange rate is the same)

92.   How many pesetas is £3.00 worth ?   (_____)

93.   How many pesetas is £12.75 worth ?   (_____)

94.   How many pesetas is £17.75 worth ?   (_____)

95.   The man buys a souvenir at 987 pesetas. How much is this in British money ? (_____)

96.   At the end of his holiday the man changes his money back into British money
      and receives £10.25. How many pesetas did he have ?   (_____)

5 people A, B, C, D and E choose 5 coloured balls from a black bag and after counting their score they put the balls back in the bag and allow the next person to choose.
The bag contains 4 red, 3 blue, 2 green and 6 white balls.
If a person chooses a green (G) ball he scores 5.
If a person chooses a red (R) ball he doubles the score of his next ball.
Consecutive red balls count as one ball.
If a person chooses a white (W) ball he scores 1.
If a person chooses a blue (B) ball he trebles the score of the ball he chose immediately before he chose the blue ball.
The person with the highest score wins the game.

The people chose these balls:

A.	G	B	W	W	R
B.	R	G	W	W	B
C.	R	R	G	W	B
D.	W	W	R	G	?
E.	R	R	W	G	G

97. What was C's score ?   (_____)

98. Who won the game ?   (_____)

99. If D scored 12, what colour was his last ball ?   (_____)

100. Which two people had the same score ?   (___&___)

TEST 13 *

1. Which letter occurs twice in INTERDICT, once in INTERCHANGE and three times in INTERDIGITAL ? (_____)

2. Which letter occurs as often in PIERCINGLY as it does in WHISTLES, but does not occur in PIGEON ? (_____)

3. Which letter occurs twice as often in DOMINEERING as it does in DONATION ? (_____)

4. Three times a number plus 5 is 44. What is twice that number minus 7 ? (_____)

5. Throughout the winter a horse eats 1/3 of its bales of hay and ignores 64 bales of hay. How many bales of hay did the horse eat ? (_____)

In the questions below TWO words must change places so that the sentence makes sense. Underline the TWO words that must change places.

Look at this example: The <u>wood</u> was made of <u>table</u>.

6. The grate burned brightly in the fire.

7. The untidy papers were covered with rooms.

8. The flowers been withered because they had not had watered.

9. The puncture by the tyre was caused in a nail.

10. The postman arrived with of sackful a mail.

The table below gives some information about the addition of numbers in the left hand column to those in the top row.

Complete the table correctly.

11-15.

	+		5.02
11.			
12.	6.28	7.36	
13.		3.96	7.9
14, 15.			5.1

In each line below write in the brackets one letter which completes the word in front of and the word after the brackets.
Look at this example: ROA (D) OOR

Here D completes ROAD and begins DOOR.

16.   ARTIS (_____) ITLE

17.   SING (_____) LEGANT

18.   STAM (_____) RISON

19.   STEA (_____) ATCH

20.   GROI (_____) OURISH

In each question below one letter can be removed from the word in the first column and put into the word in the second column to give two new words. The order of the letters is not changed.
Look at this example:

THINS   TOUT   (THIN)   (STOUT)

21. BRAKE   BASS   (_____)   (_____)

22. GRANGE   RUB   (_____)   (_____)

23. LIED   MOST   (_____)   (_____)

24. POUND   HOSING   (_____)   (_____)

25. CLONE   PANE   (_____)   (_____)

In each line below underline TWO words, ONE from each side, which together make ONE correctly spelt word. The word on the left always comes first.
Look at this example:

BLACK ALL TOP   AND   **BIRD** BOY

26. BLACK   WATER   ICE   VELVET   DOWN   FALL

27. BUT   SO   CAR   LID   ICE   NATION

28. DOOR   SEE   NOT   LAMB   WAY   LAMP

29. ON   CELL   SEED   SIZE   LING   OUT

30. LIE   HAND   EAR   MAN   WIG   HAT

Write in the brackets a word that rhymes with the second word and has a similar meaning to the first word.
Look at this example: SICK   MILL   (__ILL___)

31. PIECE   IT   (_____)

32. TUG   SCHOOL   (_____)

33. WORK   SOIL   (_____)

34-38.
In the paragraph below five words are missing. Choose the most appropriate words from the lists below. One word from list A fills the space at A, one word from list B fills the space at B and so on.
<u>Underline the word you choose.</u>

The school children played happily in the (A) as the teacher sat at his desk. It was the last day of (B) and today the children would be breaking up for their Christmas Holidays. The (C) of Christmas made all the children very (D). They hoped that soon Santa would come and deliver all his (E)

A	B	C	D	E
CORRIDOR	DECEMBER	FEAR	LONELY	REINDEER
DOORWAY	WEEK	THOUGHT	GOOD	GIFTS
CLASSROOM	TODAY	PAIN	TIRED	SNOW
GARAGE	HOLIDAYS	NOISE	EXCITED	DWARFS
HALL	TERM	SADNESS	NOISY	CAKE

5 cars Saab, Nissan, Ford, Porsche and Renault take part in a car race. The Saab finishes 3 minutes ahead of the Nissan but is not first. The Porsche finishes 4 minutes behind the Ford but only 1 minute behind the Saab. The Renault is as far behind the Porsche as the Ford is in front of the Porsche.

39. Which car is third ?   (_____)

40. Which car is last ?   (_____)

41. How many minutes separate the second and the fifth cars ?   (_____)

42. How many minutes separate the Nissan and the Ford cars ?   (_____)

43. Which car is first ?   (_____)

8 people sit equally spaced around and facing a circular table. There are four boys numbered 1, 2, 3 and 4. There are four girls lettered A , B, C and D. No two boys and no two girls sit side by side.

3 is beside B on her left and opposite 4.
C is not beside number 4 or number 1.
D sits two seats away from B.

44. Who sits opposite B ?   (_____)

45. Who sits beside 1 on his left ?   (_____)

46. Who sits on the right of the person opposite D ?   (_____)

47. Is a boy or girl opposite the person two places to the left of the person opposite A ?   (_____)

48. Who sits between C and A and opposite 1 ?   (_____)

49. Who sits beside 4 on his left ?   (_____)

A television programme begins at 16.55 and lasts for 55 minutes. Sam missed the first 15 minutes but saw the rest of the programme.

50. At what time did Sam begin to watch ?   (_____)

51. At what time did the programme end ?   (_____)

52. How long did Sam watch for ?   (_____)

In a certain code some words are written as follows. (The alphabet is printed to help you.)

A B C D E F G H I J K L M N O P Q R S T U V W X Y Z

SMILED   is written as WQMPIH
TOWEL   is written as XSAIP
CHAIR   is written as GLEMV

Write the following words in code.

53. BOOKLET   (_____)

54. MONOLITH   (_____)

55. PANIC   (_____)

What are these coded words in English ?

56. FEOIVC   (_____)

57. QEGLMRI   (_____)

58. STIVIXXE   (_____)

In questions 59-64 the three words A, B and C are in alphabetical order. The word at B is missing and you are given a dictionary definition instead. Write the correct word in the space.

Look at this example: A) FLAP
                              B) (__FLARE__) Distress signal from a boat.
                              C) FLASH

59. A) PHOTO
    B) (_ _ _ _ _ _) A group of words.
    C) PHRENOLOGY

60. A) URAL
    B) (_ _ _ _ _) Belonging to a city.
    C) URCHIN

61. A) TIGHT
    B) (_ _ _ _) Slab of baked clay for covering roofs.
    C) TILL

62. A) PORPOISE
    B) (_ _ _ _ _ _ _ _) Breakfast food, oatmeal boiled in water.
    C) PORT

63. A) THAN
    B) (_ _ _ _ _) To express gratitude.
    C) THAT

64. A) OUT
    B) (_ _ _ _) Egg shaped.
    C) OVEN

Six towns A, B, C, D, E and F are at the points numbered 1-6 but not in that order. The arrow points to the North.

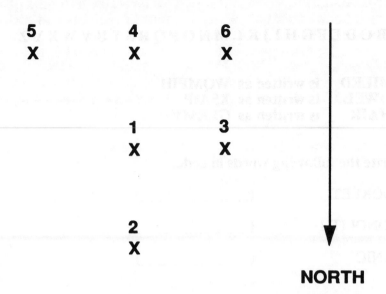

NORTH

Only one town is further North than towns A and C and this is not town D. Town B is due East of town F and due South of another town, which is not town C.

65. Which town is at point number 1 ?   (_____)

66. Which town is at point number 2 ?   (_____)

67. Which town is at point number 3 ?   (_____)

68. Which town is at point number 4 ?   (_____)

69. Which town is at point number 5 ?   (_____)

70. Which town is at point number 6 ?   (_____)

The words below and those in the lists are alike in some way. Write the letter of the list that each word belongs to in the brackets. Each letter may be used only once.

A	B	C	D	E
CASHEW	PLUTO	FERMANAGH	RICE	ALASKA
ALMOND	MINNIE	ANTRIM	WHEAT	NEBRASKA
BRAZIL	MICKEY	TYRONE	BARLEY	HAWAII

71.   DOWN   (_____)

72.   MILLET   (_____)

73.   UTAH   (_____)

74.   PEANUT   (_____)

75.   DUMBO   (_____)

TEST 13 PAGE 5.

Four boys Alan, Bill, Colin and David each receive four gifts of a toy car, a bicycle, a book and a ball. There are four of each toy and each toy comes in one of four colours. The colours are yellow, red, green and blue. Each boy has four different coloured toys and no two boys have the same toy in the same colour.

Alan's car, Bill's ball and Colin's bicycle are all the same colour. David's book is yellow. Colin's car, Bill's bicycle and Alan's book are all the same colour. David's ball is green and his bicycle is not red. Bill's car is blue and his book is not yellow or green. Colin's book is blue.

76. Who has a blue ball and a red bicycle ? (＿＿＿＿＿)

77. Who has the green bicycle ? (＿＿＿＿＿)

78. What colour is Colin's ball ? (＿＿＿＿＿)

79. What colour is Bill's bicycle ? (＿＿＿＿＿)

80. Who has a red book ? (＿＿＿＿＿)

81. Who has a green car ? (＿＿＿＿＿)

In each question 82-85 the numbers in the second column are formed from the numbers in the first column by using a certain rule. Put the correct answer opposite the arrow. A different rule is used in each question.

82. 9 ----> 35
    11 ----> 41
    7 ----> 29
    4 ---->

83. 2.55 ----> 4.20
    5.35 ----> 7.00
    4.80 ----> 6.45
    1.35 ---->

84. 3 ----> 18
    5 ----> 34
    7 ----> 58
    9 ---->

85. 4.1 ----> 2.05
    3.5 ----> 1.45
    6.15 ----> 4.1
    5.6 ---->

Using the numbers 2,7,5 and 6 once only in each question fill in the spaces in any way which makes the statements correct.

86. (＿＿ + ＿＿ - ＿＿) X ＿＿ = 24

87. (＿＿ + ＿＿) - (＿＿ + ＿＿) = 4

88. (＿＿ + ＿＿ + ＿＿) ÷ ＿＿ = 3

89. (＿＿ X ＿＿) + (＿＿ X ＿＿) = 47

90. (＿＿ X ＿＿) + (＿＿ + ＿＿) = 39

Complete these sequences, the alphabet is printed to help you.

A B C D E F G H I J K L M N O P Q R S T U V W X Y Z

91. C, F, H, K, M,   (_____)

92. BZV, FXU, JVT, NTS,   (_____)

93. S, T, R, U, Q, V,   (_____)

94. T, R, N, H,   (_____)

95. M, O, K, Q, I, S,   (_____)

Five garages A, B, C, D and E have a different number of cars for sale. No garage has less than 3 cars or more than 12 cars. The total number of cars is 36. Only one garage has an even number of cars for sale.

The cars of D and E added together give 2 more than C's cars. D has 3 times as many cars as B who has 4 less than A.

96. How many cars has A for sale ?   (_____)

97. How many cars has B for sale ?   (_____)

98. How many cars has C for sale ?   (_____)

99. How many cars has D for sale ?   (_____)

100. How many cars has E for sale ?   (_____)

TEST 14 *

1. Which letter appears the same number of times in the words DECISION and
    KESTREL ?   (_____)

2. Which letter occurs twice as often in NARCISSISM as it does in STOCKIST ? (_____)

3. Which letter occurs less often in COMMISSION than in CLASSICAL ?   (_____)

4. In a garden there are three types of flowers. One third of them are roses. A quarter
    of the rest are carnations. There are 30 asters in the garden. How many carnations
    are there ?   (_____)

5. Tom has 45p. If John had 12p more he would have the same as Peter. If Tom
    spent one third of his money he would also have the same as Peter.   How much
    does John have ?   (_____)

**In the sentences below 2 words must change places to make the sentences
sensible. Underline the TWO words. An example is shown.**

The <u>wood</u> is made of <u>table</u>.

6. The girl pavement a cat on the drew.

7. A pound pond fell into a coin.

8. Minor fog caused many dense accidents.

9. Without failed the radio batteries to work.

10. The clock was slow six minutes nearly this morning.

11. I help already done it without any have.

**The table below gives some information about the addition of numbers in
the left hand column to numbers in the top row. Complete the table.**

12.

13, 14, 15.

16, 17.

+	7.6		5.8
		9.7	
3.4		11.2	

TEST 14 PAGE 1.

In each question write in the brackets one letter which will complete both the word in front of the brackets and the word after the brackets.

Here is an example.   ROA (D) OOR.

18. ACOR ( ) ASTY   19. EMI ( ) URF

20. SING ( ) ACH   21. PATI ( ) ATH

22. SPIR   ( ) QUAL   23. VER ( ) ULB

In each line below a word from the left-hand group joins one from the right-hand group to make a new word. The left-hand word comes first. Underline the chosen words.   An example has been done to help you.

	CORN	FARM	TIME		OVER	FIELD	YARD
24.	GET	REST	OFF		FULL	LESS	HER
25.	OR	TRY	SIN		FARE	RING	DEAL
26.	FUR	MET	MORE		HOD	ALL	LEG
27.	CAB	SIT	TRIP		PET	LET	ILL
28.	MIST	OR	CAN		BUT	ERR	RUST
29.	ART	LET	SEA		PING	SON	HER

In the following questions a letter can be taken from the first word and put into the second word to form TWO new words. Write both NEW words.

Example. THEN   TANK   (TEN) (THANK)

The H moves from THEN to TANK and makes the new words TEN and THANK.

30. PAINT   NOSE   (_____) (_____)

31. MORE   PAPER   (_____) (_____)

32. TAINT   NET   (_____) (_____)

33. FACTORY   FLING   (_____) (_____)

34. TABLE   GARAGE   (_____) (_____)

35. DINNER   DOOR   (_____) (_____)

Five patients, a man, woman, boy, girl and baby are waiting to see a doctor. The girl is behind the baby but before the boy. The man is before the woman and she is one before the last. The girl is behind the man but he is not first. List the patients in order.

36. First.   (_____)

37. Second.   (_____)

38. Third.   (_____)

39. Fourth.   (_____)

40. Fifth.   (_____)

In the sentences below there are 6 words missing. From the lists A to F choose the **MOST SUITABLE** words to complete the sentences. Choose a word from list A to fill space A, a word from list B to fill space B and so on. **Underline the chosen word in each group.**

The unicorn is an (A) animal that never lived. It was (B) to have the body of a horse with a single horn (C) the middle of its forehead. It was said that a unicorn could be (D) if someone stood in front of a tree and (E) aside as it charged. The horn would then become (F) in the tree.

A	B	C	D	E	F
foolish	meant	at	found	went	scraped
extinct	only	beside	frightened	walked	stuck
imaginary	intended	over	caught	jumped	bent
funny	always	in	discovered	hopped	sharpened
savage	supposed	behind	angered	stood	scored

41.   42.   43.   44.   45.   46.

Six children stand equally spaced in a circle and are numbered from 1 to 6 in a clockwise direction. Number 2 stands between 1 and 3.
Number 3 stands between 2 and 4, and so on.
The smallest odd number and the largest even number change places.
The other two odd numbers then change places. The two numbers which add together to make a total of 4 change places.
Finally the two numbers which add to make 10 change places.

47. Which number did not change to a different position ?   (_____)

48. Which number finished where number 5 started ?   (_____)

49. Which number finished where number 1 started ?   (_____)

50. Which number finished standing between 6 and 2 ?   (_____)

51. Which number finished standing between 1 and 4 ?   (_____)

↑ **NORTH**

*
52

The positions of 6 towns are shown.
The towns are A,B,C,D,E and F.

Town F is further to the north than
town E but is not the most northerly town.

B is directly south of one town and
directly west of another.

*   *
53   54

Town A is south-east of C which is
south-west of another town.

*   *
55   56

*
57

In the brackets enter the letter for each town.

52. (_____)   53. (_____)   54. (_____)

55. (_____)   56. (_____)   57. (_____)

WAIT   HAM   LACK   VIEW   OFF   TRAY   BEE
MOAN   LIAR   MIGHT   TONGUE ONE

From the list above choose a word which rhymes with each of the following.
Write the rhyming words in the brackets.

58. WHACK   (_____)   59. CHOIR   (_____)

60. FREIGHT   (_____)   61. COUGH   (_____)

62. LAMB   (_____)   63. QUEUE   (_____)

64. BONE   (_____)   65. QUAY   (_____)

Complete the following sequences. The alphabet is printed to help you.

A B C D E F G H I J K L M N O P Q R S T U V W X Y Z

66. B   D   G   K   P   (_____)

67. A   D   F   I   K   (_____)

68. CZE   DYF   EXG   FWH   (GVI__)

69. EXF   HUI   KRL   NOO   (_____)

70. DWL   MEX   YNF   GZO   (_____)

71. ZA   CU   QF   JN   (_____)

In a code **2 3 4 6 1** and **1 2 3 4 5** represent two of the words

ROPES   PORTS   SPORT   POSER   SPORE .

Write each word in code.

72. ROPES   (_____)
73. PORTS   (_____)
74. SPORT   (_____)
75. POSER   (_____)
76. SPORE   (_____)

Decode the following.

77. 2 4 3 6 5 1 6   (_____)
78. 4 5 1 3 4 6   (_____)
79. 2 3 1 6 5 4 1   (_____)

The diagram below is made up of two triangles, a rhombus, a square, a rectangle and a parallelogram. By joining the points F I J, one of the triangles is made.

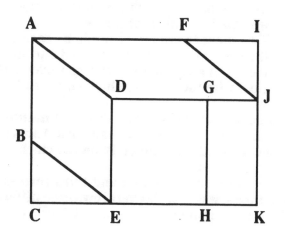

80. Which points join together to make up the other triangle ?   (_____)

81. Which points join together to make up the square ?   (_____)

82. Which points join together to make up the rhombus ?   (_____)

83. Which points join together to make up the rectangle ?   (_____)

84. Which points join together to make up the parallelogram ?   (_____)

Five children, A, B, C, D and E have each saved a different amount of money. No one has saved less than £20 or more than £30.
A has £3 more than C but less money than D.
Only A and E have an even amount of money.
B has the smallest amount, which is £7 less than E has.
Only one child has saved more than E.

How much has each child saved ?

85. A has saved £_____   86. B has saved £_____

87. C has saved £_____   88. D has saved £_____

89. E has saved £_____

Four girls, Ann, Betty, Clare and Dawn played a game using the face of a clock. Each girl had a counter which was moved around the numbers on the clock face.

RULES   A die (a single dice) was thrown and the number shown was the number on which the counter was placed. No further move was made at this first throw.
Two more throws were made by each girl. If an odd number was thrown, the counter was moved anti-clockwise that number of moves. If an even number was thrown, the counter was moved clockwise the number shown on the die.

The game began and each girl threw a different number with her first throw. No one threw a 4 or a 1 at this stage. All Ann's throws were even numbers and she finished on number 10 on the clock face. Her second and third throws were the same.
Clare finished on number 2. Her first and third throws were odd numbers and her second throw was a 4. Dawn threw three different odd numbers. Betty threw the same number each time and finished where she started.

90. On which number did Dawn finish ?   (_____)

91. On which number did Betty finish ?   (_____)

92. What was Ann's second throw ?   (_____)

93. What was Clare's third throw ?   (_____)

If each girl had been given one more throw -

94. What would Dawn have needed to finish on number 5 ?   (_____)

95. What would Betty have needed to finish on number 1 ?   (_____)

Using the numbers 3, 4, 5 and 6 ONCE ONLY in each question, fill in the spaces in any way that will make the statements correct. An example is shown to help you.

$$\underline{3} + \underline{4} \qquad + \underline{5} + \underline{6} \qquad = \quad 18.$$

96. (___ + ___)   -   (___ - ___)   = 6.

97. (___ + ___ + ___) X ___   = 45.

98. (___ + ___)   X   (___ - ___)   = 11.

99. (___ X ___)   -   (___ - ___)   = 11.

100. (___ - ___)   +   (___ X ___)   = 31.

TEST 15

SCORE _____

1. Which letter appears three times in ENCHANTING and twice in NATIONALITY ? (____)

2. Which letter appears twice in CONCENTRATES but not at all in RECESSION? (____)

3. Which letter occurs as many times in UNYEILDING as it does in PRACTICE ? (____)

4. When three is subtracted from seven times a number the answer is 53. What is the number ? (____)

5. Twice 18 is the same as four times a number. What is the number ? (____)

A comic and two packets of crisps costs 50p. A comic and one packet of crisps costs 36p.

6. How much is a comic ? (____)

7. How much is a packet of crisps ? (____)

In the sentences below 2 words must change places to make the sentences sensible. Underline the TWO words. An example is shown.

The <u>wood</u> is made of <u>table</u>.

8. There for no key was the back door.

9. Have you spend money left to any ?

10. Under the strain great cord broke.

11. Running not the corridor is in allowed.

12. Was supermarket checkout every very busy.

13. Under lay scattered books the table.

The table below gives some information about the subtraction of numbers in the left hand column from numbers in the top row. Complete the table.

	—	9.96		
14, 15.				
16, 17.	2.73		4.12	
18, 19.		5.14		3.15

In each question write in the brackets one letter which will complete both the word in front of the brackets and the word after the brackets.

Here is an example.   ROA (D) OOR.

20. MAL   ( ) ONE   21. CAS ( ) USH

22. TAME   ( ) ORE   23. LEA ( ) LOD

24. SOL   ( ) IGHT   25. SOD ( ) GAIN

In each line below a word from the left-hand group joins one from the right-hand group to make a new word. The left-hand word comes first. Underline the chosen words.   An example has been done to help you.

CORN	**FARM**	TIME		OVER	FIELD	**YARD**

26.	JUST	SAT	TAKE	TAN	ICE	OR
27.	PAST	COMB	TOLD	AT	YOUR	MINE
28.	UP	OVER	DOWN	PAIR	SIT	HOLD
29.	SAD	CAT	AM	ILL	BUSH	ALE
30.	BUT	WAG	TO	ON	ERR	WERE
31.	USE	SAT	ACT	FULL	TING	OR

In the following questions a letter can be taken from the first word and put into the second word to form TWO new words. Write both NEW words.

Example. THEN   TANK   (TEN) (THANK)

The H moves from THEN to TANK and makes the new words TEN and THANK.

32.   CANOE   SHUT   (_____)   (_____)

33.   FLAKE   HALO   (_____)   (_____)

34.   LEAD   SIZE   (_____)   (_____)

35.   THREAT   SOW   (_____)   (_____)

36.   CADGE   LAY   (_____)   (_____)

37.   BALD   DARING   (_____)   (_____)

Roy is 6 years older than Harry who is 3 years younger than Ian.
Ian is 2 years older than Tom who is 4 years older than Sam.
Tom is 11 and Colin is 14.
List the boys in order from the youngest.

38. Youngest.   (_____)

39.   (_____)

40.   (_____)

41.   (_____)

42.   (_____)

43. Oldest.   (_____)

Groups of words are printed below. Each group is made up of words which are similar in some way.

A	B	C	D	E	F
daffodil	leopard	tango	penny farthing	kestrel	madam
daisy	puma	waltz	unicycle	hawk	tot
tulip	tiger	jive	bicycle	falcon	deed

Decide into which of the above groups the following words would fit. Write the group letter in the brackets.

44. tandem   (_____)   45. orchid   (_____)

46. ewe   (_____)   47. merlin   (_____)

48. ballet   (_____)   49. panther   (_____)

In a code words are written as shown below.

APPLE becomes DSSOH   WEATHER becomes ZHDWKHU

Write the following words in code. The alphabet is printed to help you.

A B C D E F G H I J K L M N O P Q R S T U V W X Y Z

50. PORCUPINE (_____)   51. WISDOM (_____)

52. EXCEPT   (_____)

Decode the following words.

53. KBSKHQ   (_____)   54. FRQIOLFW (_____)

55. RUJDQLF   (_____)   56. UDGLVK   (_____)

Six children, A, B, C, D, E and F stand equally spaced in a circle.
They face into the centre of the circle.
Another child G, stands in the centre of the circle.
G is looking directly at B. D is between A and F.
A is not standing next to B nor is directly behind G.
E is standing to the left of A.

57. Who is standing directly behind G ?   (_____)

58. Who is to the left of F ?   (_____)

59. Who is to the right of F ?   (_____)

60 - 61. Apart from B, which two children can G see ?   (_____,_____)

V, W, X, Y and Z are five books.
V and X are story books and the others are non-fiction.
X and Y are not for children but the others are.
W and Y are not paperbacks but the rest are.

62. Which hardbacked book is a non-fiction adult book ? (_____)

63. Which paperback book is a children's story book ?   (_____)

64. Which adult paperback is a story book ?   (_____)

65. Is there a children's paperbacked non-fiction book ?   (_____)

66. Is there an adult's hardbacked story book ?   (_____)

In the following questions the numbers in the second column are formed
from the numbers in the first column by using the same rule. Put the
correct answer in the brackets for each question.

67. 1 ----> 6   68. 11 ----> 25   69. 2 ----> 5

     3 ----> 12   8 ----> 19   6 ----> 15

     6 ----> 21   5 ----> 13   8 ----> 20

     9 ----> (____)   0 ----> (____)   11 ---> (____)

70. 1 ----> 5   71. 4 ----> 1   72. 2 ----> 3

     4 ----> 20   10 ----> 4   6 ----> 9

     6 ----> 40   16 ----> 7   10 ----> 15

     7 ----> (____)   22 ----> (____)   14 ----> (____)

In each of the following questions 3 words are in alphabetical order.
The second word has not been written but its meaning is given.
Decide what the second word should be each time and write it in the
brackets. Each dash in the brackets represents a letter.
An example is shown to help you.

CROSS

(C R O W D) a large group of people.

CRUEL

73. NEWT

(_ _ _ _ _ _) to take small bites.

NICKNAME

74. TEXTILE

(_ _ _ _ _) upper part of leg.

TIDAL

75. FOAM

(_ _ _ _ _) adjust to get a clear image.

FOUNDATION

76. SCREEN

(_ _ _ _ _ _ _ _) write in a careless way.

SCRUB

77. MAMMAL

(_ _ _ _ _ _ _) large dwelling house.

MARCH

78. WEASEL

(_ _ _ _ _) mammal which lives in the sea.

WHEEL

TEST 15 PAGE 5.

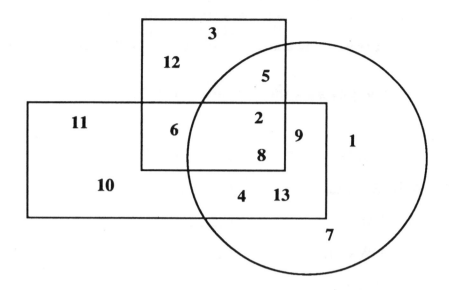

The following questions are about the numbers in the diagram above.

79. Which numbers appear in all three figures ?   (_____)

80. Which number is in both the circle and square but not in the rectangle ?   (_____)

81. Which numbers are in both the circle and rectangle but not in the square ? (_____)

82. Find the sum of all the numbers which appear in one figure only.   (_____)

83. Take the sum of the numbers that are in the square, but not the rectangle,
    from the sum of the numbers that are in the circle but not the square.   (_____)

84. Take the sum of the numbers that are in the circle, but not the rectangle or
    square, from the sum of the numbers that are in the rectangle, but not the
    circle or square.   (_____)

In the questions below give the next number in each series.

85.	37	21	13	9	7	(_____)
86.	1.9	3.7	5.5	7.3	9.1	(_____)
87.	1	8	27	64	125	(_____)
88.	3	8	18	38	78	(_____)
89.	2.75	4	5.25	6.5	7.75	(_____)
90.	(2,6)	(5,10)	(8,14)	(11,18)		(___,___)

In a car park there are 250 cars.
The cars are coloured BLUE, WHITE, RED, YELLOW and BLACK.
For every one blue car there are four white cars.
There are twice as many red cars as white cars.
For every yellow car there are three white cars.
There are as many black cars as there are yellow and blue cars together.

How many cars are there of each colour ?

91. BLUE CARS   (_____)

92. WHITE CARS   (_____)

93. RED CARS   (_____)

94. YELLOW CARS   (_____)

95. BLACK CARS   (_____)

Three football teams wear jerseys, shorts and socks.
Each article is in either red, white or black.
No team has more than one article of any colour.
No team wears an article in the same colour as another team.
The teams are called Rovers, City and United.

Rovers' jersey is either black or red.
United's socks and City's shorts are the same colour - either red or white.
United's jersey, City's socks and Rovers' shorts are all the same colour - either white or red.

State the colour of each of the following.

96. United's shorts ?   (_____)

97. City's socks ?   (_____)

98. City's jersey ?   (_____)

99. Rovers' jersey ?   (_____)

100. Rovers' socks ?   (_____)

ANSWERS TO TEST 11

#			#		
1.	E or R or both		51.	EMERY	
2.	D or G or both		52.	ENAMEL	
3.	E		53.	ENCLOSE	
4.	8		54.	2.00	
5.	10		55.	2.05	
6.	5		56.	2.40	
7.	5		57.	LATER	THICK
8.	FAN	CAR	58.	FORD	BAIT
9.	RAIN	TOP	59.	RISE	KNIT
10.	SAILED	LIFTED	60.	LANE	CHARM
11.	NOTE	TORN	61.	THEM	GALLERY
12.	DINNER	ARE	62.	MAZE	NOISE
13.	3.8		63.	203	
14.	3		64.	534	
15.	3.4		65.	SOUTH	
16.	2.6		66.	SOUTH	
17.	M		67.	NORTH	
18.	B, M, P, R or T		68.	D	
19.	Y		69.	C	
20.	P		70.	F	
21.	G		71.	E	
22.	D or T		72.	A	
23.	K		73.	E	
24.	HG		74.	D	
25.	BCD		75.	C	
26.	ON		76.	A and E	
27.	7.5		77.	10	
28.	9		78.	MID	
29.	2		79.	GUN	
30.	14.2		80.	DOWN	
31.	FOR	SAKE	81.	OVER	
32.	DAM	PEN	82.	18	2X
33.	JERK	IN	83.	6	Sq root X-1
34.	PAD DOCK or PASS ABLE		84.	36	2X + 2
35.	TAB	LET	85.	2	Half of (X-2)
36.	MAN	OR	86.	125	X Cubed
37.	MISERABLE		87.	27	3X - 3
38.	HUDDLED		88.	1/2	
39.	WARM		89.	1/2	
40.	SEARCH		90.	HALL	HULL*
41.	4		91.	PINE	PANE*
42.	7		92.	FACE	LACE*
43.	2		93.	HERB	HERD*
44.	3		94.	CHIP	SHIP*
45.	1		95.	E	
46.	7.5 or 71/2		96.	J	
47.	7		97.	A	
48.	-1		98.	Z	
49.	EMEND		99.	O	
50.	EMERGE		100.	I	

* There may be other possible answers.

ANSWERS TO TEST 12

#			#		
1.	N		51.	00.09 24HR CLOCK	
2.	I or G		52.	0.55(-0.9)	
3.	W		53.	(62,11)(+7,8)	
4.	27		54.	47(+5,7.9 ETC)	
5.	13p		55.	4 (÷ by 4)	
6.	TELEVISION	CHILD	56.	(8X6)-(5X4) *	
7.	PICTURE	FRAMED	57.	(6+5+8)X 4 *	
8.	SUN	PAINT	58.	(8-5)-(6-4) *	
9.	PROGRAM	OPERATOR	59.	(8+5)X(6+4) *	
10.	PRESENT	MOTHER	60.	(6X4)-(8+5) *	
11.	5.1		61.	ANXIOUS	
12.	2.5		62.	PLAGUE	
13.	22.7		63.	FOUNTAIN	
14.	27.3		64.	HIRE	
15.	35.95		65.	JACKAL	
16.	28.75		66.	MOUTH	
17.	N		67.	65 (XSQ+1)	
18.	G		68.	35 1.25x	
19.	E		69.	35 (7X-7)	
20.	R		70.	272 (3X+2)	
21.	L		71.	B,C, E	
22.	HAROLD		72.	B,C **	
23.	GEORGE		73.	D, E	
24.	WILLIAM		74.	D	
25.	ALFRED		75.	741235	
26.	CHARLES		76.	512351	
27.	AS SENT		77.	61234	
28.	BOOK CASE		78.	REAPER	
29.	PAGE ANT		79.	PEARL	
30.	STIR RING		80.	LABEL	
31.	SUIT OR		81.	PETER	
32.	VICAR AGE		82.	BILLY	
33.	10		83.	PETER	
34.	6		84.	YELLOW	
35.	3		85.	YELLOW	
36.	3		86.	YELLOW	
37.	1		87.	40cms	
38.	REPLY		88.	100sq.cms	
39.	RAISE		89.	180 tiles	
40.	MOB		90.	64 tiles	
41.	EXPLODED		91.	£3.32	
42.	OCTOBER		92.	564 pesetas	
43.	GASPED		93.	2397 pesetas	
44.	CASCADE		94.	3337 pesetas	
45.	DARK		95.	£5.25	
46.	TEAT	PRINT	96.	1927 pesetas	
47.	FIN	DRUM	97.	13	
48.	VICE	OWING	98.	A	
49.	GASH	LINEN	99.	RED	
50.	BACK	RULE	100.	D and E	

* Other combinations may be correct
** A square is a rectangle with 4 equal sides.

These are the answers to Book 3 of a set of 4 graded books. A child who has not previously attempted questions of this type may have difficulty with the first few tests. However, research shows that a child's ability to handle and understand these questions generally increases with practice.

ANSWERS TO TEST 13

1. I
2. L
3. I
4. 19
5. 32
6. GRATE
7. PAPERS   FIRE
8. BEEN   ROOMS
9. BY   HAD
10. OF   IN
11. 1.08   A
12. 11.3
13. 2.88
14. 0.08
15. 1.16
16. T
17. E
18. P
19. L or M .
20. N
21. BAKE
22. RANGE
23. LED
24. POND
25. CONE
26. WATER   PANEL/PLANE
27. CAR   NATION/SO   LID
28. DOOR   MOIST
29. SEED   WAY
30. EAR   LING
31. BIT   WIG
32. PULL
33. TOIL
34. CLASSROOM
35. TERM
36. THOUGHT
37. EXCITED
38. GIFTS
39. PORSCHE
40. RENAULT
41. 5 mins.
42. 6 mins
43. FORD
44. A
45. B
46. 3
47. GIRL
48. 2
49. D
50. 17.10
51. 17.50
52. 40 mins
53. FSSOPIX
54. QSRSPMXL
55. TERMG
56. BAKERY
57. MACHINE
58. OPERETTA
59. PHRASE
60. URBAN
61. TILE
62. PORRIDGE
63. THANK
64. OVAL
65. A
66. E
67. C
68. C
69. B
70. D
71. F
72. C
73. D
74. E
75. A
76. B
77. ALAN
78. BILL
79. RED
80. GREEN
81. BILL
82. COLIN
83. 20 (3x +8)
84. 3.0 (+ 1.65)
85. 90 (XSQ. +9)
86. 3.55 (-2.05)
87. (2+7-5) X 6 *
88. (2+7) - (2+6) *
89. (7+5) - (2+6) *
90. (7+6+2) ÷ 5 *
91. (7X5) + (2X6) *
92. (5X6) + (2+7) *
93. RRR
94. P
95. Z
96. G
97. G
98. 7
99. 3
100. 5

* Other combinations may be correct.

ANSWERS TO TEST 14

1. S
2. I
3. C
4. 7
5. 18
6. PAVEMENT   DREW
7. POND   COIN
8. MINOR   DENSE
9. FAILED   BATTERIES
10. SLOW   NEARLY
11. HELP   HAVE
12. 7.8
13. 1.9
14. 9.5
15. 7.7
16. 11.0
17. 9.2
18. N
19. T
20. E
21. O
22. E
23. B
24. A   REST   LESS
25. OR   DEAL
26. MET   HOD
27. TRIP   LET
28. MIST   RUST
29. SEA   SON
30. PANT   NOISE
31. ORE   NEAT
32. TINT   PAMPER
33. FACTOR   FLYING
34. TALE   GARBAGE
35. DINER   DONOR
36. BABY
37. MAN
38. GIRL
39. WOMAN
40. BOY
41. IMAGINARY
42. SUPPOSED
43. IN
44. CAUGHT
45. JUMPED
46. STUCK
47. 2
48. 1
49. 4
50. 5
51. 3
52. D
53. C
54. F
55. B
56. A
57. E
58. LACK
59. LIAR
60. WAIT
61. OFF
62. HAM
63. VIEW
64. MOAN
65. BEE
66. V
67. N
68. GVI
69. QLR
70. PHA
71. LO
72. E
73. 43251
74. 12346
75. 23154
76. 12345
77. RESORT
78. PROTEST
79. POSTERS
80. BCE *
81. DGHE *
82. ADEB *
83. GJKH *
84. AFJD *
85. 26
86. 21
87. 23
88. 29
89. 28
90. 1
91. 6
92. 4
93. 5
94. 4
95. 5, 4, 6, 3 **
96. 4, 5, 6, 3 **
97. 4, 5, 4, 3 **
98. 6, 5, 4, 3 **
99. 3, 4, 6, 5 **
100. 4, 3, 6, 5 **

* Different letter order may be correct.
** Other combinations may work.

ANSWERS TO TEST 15

1. N
2. T
3. E
4. 8
5. 9
6. 22
7. 14.
8. FOR   WAS
9. SPEND   ANY
10. THE   GREAT
11. NOT   IN
12. WAS   EVERY
13. UNDER   BOOKS
14. 6.85
15. 7.97
16. 7.23
17. 5.24
18. 4.82
19. 2.03
20. T or L
21. H
22. S
23. P
24. E
25. A
26. JUST   ICE
27. COMB   AT
28. UP   HOLD
29. AM   BUSH
30. WAG   ON
31. ACT   OR
32. CANE   SHOUT
33. FAKE   HALLO
34. LAD   SEIZE
35. TREAT   SHOW
36. CAGE   LADY
37. BAD   DARLING
38. SAM
39. HARRY
40. TOM
41. IAN
42. COLIN
43. ROY
44. D
45. A
46. F
47. E
48. C
49. B
50. BLACK
51. ZLVGRP
52. HAFHSW
53. HYPHEN
54. CONFLICT
55. ORGANIC
56. RADISH
57. D
58. D
59. C
60&61. E + C
62. Y
63. V
64. X   3X + 3
65. YES   2X + 3
66. NO
67. 30
68. 3
69. 27.5   2.5X   XSQ + 4
70. 53.   2.5X   (X:2) -1
71. 10   1.5X
72. 21
73. NIBBLE
74. THIGH
75. FOCUS
76. SCRIBBLE
77. MANSION
78. WHALE
79. 2.8
80. 5
81. 4, 9, 13
82. 44
83. 14
84. 13
85. 6
86. 10.9
87. 216
88. 158
89. 9
90. 14, 22
91. 15
92. 60
93. 120
94. 20
95. 35
96. BLACK
97. WHITE
98. BLACK
99. RED
100. BLACK